Special Agent Anonymoose
Personnel File:

Size: Extremely large

Distinguishing features:
Antlers, dark brown
hide, small birthmark
that looks a little like
North Dakota

Talents: Master of disguise, spying,
investigating the strange (and
possibly strange) goings-on in Woodland
Territories; surprisingly a world-
renowned Twister player

Favorite drink: Chocolate milk—
shaken, not stirred

Clearance for spying:
First Class Spy Clearance
for secrets

Clearance for height:
About seven and a half feet

Math for fun!
$\sqrt{4} \div 7 + 1.3946$

$\times 8$
$=$
$\downarrow$
carry
the
one
$=$
52

Not-Quite-So-Special Agent Owlfred Personnel File:

Size: Small enough that he can fit in a moose's pocket

Distinguishing features: Gray, feathery, can do that weird owl thing where they twist their head most of the way around (but it makes him slightly motion sick)

Talents: Very precise analysis of clues and data, calm attitude in a crisis, patience in a crisis (also very good at just avoiding a crisis)

Favorite drink: Hot cocoa with extra chocolate

Clearance for spying: Third Class Spy Clearance for secrets

Clearance for height: Irrelevant due to flying and all

To-Do List

• Hot chocolate (lots)
• Solve mystery

Chapter 1

★ NEWS OF THE WILD ★

MOOSE MISJUDGES MANIC MOON MAYHEM

"NO COMMENT," SAID MOOSE.

OCTOPUS WINS PRIZE

SHAKEN AND STIRRED

Agent Moose, your mission is to investigate a missing animal—Terrance Turtle. He was a witness in the recent high-profile robbery case that your esteemed colleague and fellow agent Camo Chameleon just solved. It was his 100th case. We're throwing him a little party to celebrate down in South Shore where he's based.

We thought it would work out well. You could attend the party, congratulate Camo Chameleon on being the best agent at Woodland HQ, and then nip off and find this missing witness.

AGENT MOOSE

Flamingo Fandango

Well, there's a case about a turtle...

Congratulations, Camo!

Did that coat rack just talk? Hang on. Seven foot, brown, furry...? Anonymoose?

Flamingo Fandango

Chapter 3

BIRD'S-EYE VIEW

AGENT MOOSE

We were wondering if you knew anything about a turtle?

We know lots of turtles. There's Tuco the pink-bellied side-neck turtle.

"Ouch. Can you pass me the sunblock? I think I got a little too much sun on my belly."

Oh, and the slider turtle twins—Tom and Tanya...

"I bet you I can drop down that dune faster! No way! Eat my sand!! Whoooo heeee!"

Those kids. Always racing somewhere.

Bird's-Eye View

AGENT MOOSE

Ahhhhh!!

Ahhhhh! Ummm. Excuse me. Why are we doing this "Ahhhh" thing, Miss Mermaid?

Ahhhh! Sorry. I thought you were going to try to eat me.

Oh.

You're not going to try to eat me, are you?

I don't think so.

Good. Very good. Okay. So, I'm just going to sit here, then. Without shouting.

Okay.

Ahhhhh!!

Like, I might wonder for instance...why is an owl floating on a billboard in the bay with his head through a mermaid poster?

!

You mean she's not a real mermaid?

He has feathers on his face. Do you know any mermaids with feathers on their face?

I don't know any mermaids, actually, so I was keeping an open mind.

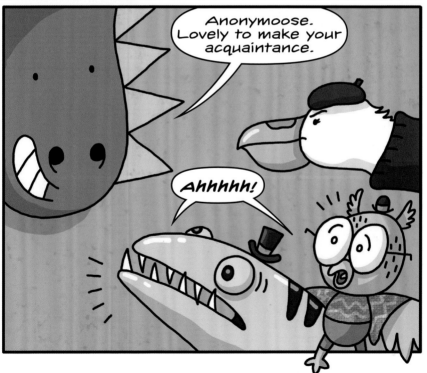

AGENT MOOSE

Ahhhhh!!

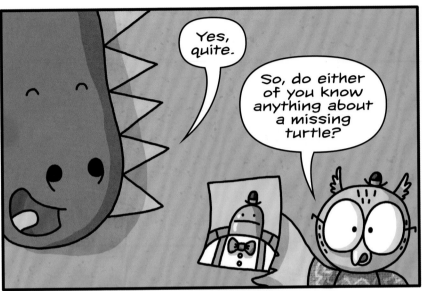

Yes, quite.

So, do either of you know anything about a missing turtle?

Sometimes folks just disappear and are never seen again.

Yeah, that's the way it is in South Shore. Sometimes it's better to leave things as they are rather than mess with them. If you know what I mean?

I think I do. ≥gulp≤ Thank you for your time. We really have to be going, don't we, Anonymoose?

Do we?

Yes!!!

But I would like to speak with your new friends...

Ahhhhh!!

I think you two are better off just enjoying the sights around here. Not everyone likes someone sticking a beak into their business.

Glare!

Phew!

I thought >pant< they were going to >pant< eat me!

Both of them? Not likely. They did not want to talk turtle though. Hmmm. Definitely animals of...

interest.

This Is a Strange Day

AGENT MOOSE

Chapter 6

GOOD OWL/BAD MOOSE

Now, I'm sure that this is where we last spotted him.

So, if you think that Barry is in on the turtle-napping, what makes you think that he won't just owl-nap me?

I suppose he could. Good point. Wait, shhh. I see something in the water.

Snip Snip!

AHHHHHH!

Ahoy-hoy!

Hi there, feathered mermaid! Are we doing the "Ahhhh!" thing again? 'Cause I had a sore throat after all that "Ahhhhhing" before.

Sorry that last "Ahhh" just came out.

Is that anything like chocolate mousse?

Not really.

Well, you are both brown?

Aside from the color, I am completely different from chocolate mousse.

That's a shame. I like chocolate mousse. Especially in the little gold shiny wrappers.

Right...

Good Owl/Bad Moose

AGENT MOOSE

You can't. Why don't I be Reasonable Owl and you can be Frantic-Confused-but-Uncannily-Successful-at-Saving-the-World Moose like always?

So much patience...

Good plan. I like that moose.

I still like chocolate mousse better.

Good Owl/Bad Moose

So, Barry, we want the facts about Terrance the Turtle.

BAD OWL! →

Well... I don't know him but I suppose he's a turtle... and his mother liked the name Terrance? Or maybe it was a family name, you know, like Barry. My mom hated the name Barry but my dad was a Barry Barracuda and his dad was a Barry Barracuda and his dad...

You mean you don't know anything about Terrance the Turtle's disappearance?

You're innocent?

Turtle-napped

So, what do we do if the turtle-napper tries to turtle-nap us?

We catch him, of course, and bring him to justice. After the party maybe? Well, it depends on the time, I suppose.

Let me check my watch. I just tucked it into my shell. Hang on...

Shoop!

Turtle-napped

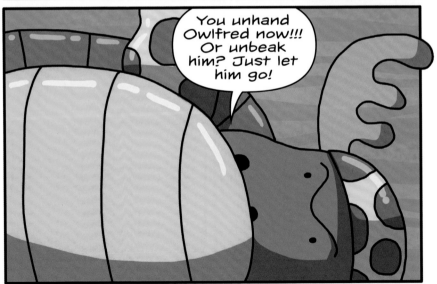

✦ Still struggling! ✦

Excuse me, Mr. Exceptionally Large Turtle? There was a moose asking us about a missing turtle earlier...

You wouldn't happen to be named Terrance, would you?

It's me, parrots! Anonymoose! I'm disguised as a turtle, and that pelican just turtle-napped Owlfred.

The coconut?

Yes, but he's an owl, and he was just turtle-napped.

Did you hit your head with all that rolling around?

Okay, think, Anonymoose... What would Owlfred do?

Tap!

Paper-work!

Dress as a coconut?

No, he would make a plan.

Not dressed as a coconut, then?

Turtle-napped

You've just given me an idea! Quick, we'll head back to the pier and you two secretly find Newt and the chipmunk. Let's get this plan into action.

Trip!

Roll!

Just as soon as I flip over again...

Buffet: 1 plate per animal

"Buffet" is one of my favorite words!

Yeah, it's breaking news. The turtle just showed up and started talking!

Go, Camo!

Oh my!

He's right here.

There are two of them!

I wanted to be extra sure. I saw another turtle who looked similar, so I thought I'd get him too. You know, just in case. But it turned out to be that Not-Quite-So-Special Agent Owl.

Gulp!

Hey!

BURP!

Blech!!!

He did it because he not only *solved* all the crimes. He *caused* all the crimes so he could get credit for solving them.

What a scoop!

You talk too much, little turtle. That's why I had to pouch you in the first place!

You caused the crimes?

To think we trusted you, Camo Chameleon. You are hereby stripped of the title Special Agent.

And you won't be getting any trophies anytime soon. Unless they give some sort of trophy for best behaved prisoner or something in Woodland Prison. But I really doubt you would win.

HUP!

smack!

AGENT MOOSE

For successfully solving your 100th case.

3 Gasp!

100 Cases Solved

I had some help from my trusty Not-Quite-So-Special Agent Owlfred and the team from the Big Woods.

Proud!

We got together and wrote a little song to celebrate... Five, six, seven eight... Who's the moose with the most? Raise your glasses! Make a toast! Thanks are due. Yes, to you. And your funky woodland crew! You can stay on South Shore. And we'll sing to you some more. But we know, you must go. Find the chameleon...named...Ca...mo!!

100 cases!

Tap!

OOHHHH YEAAAH!

★ NEWS OF THE WILD ★

SLEEPY SOUTH SHORE SHOCKED by CALAMITOUS CHAMELEON CAPERS in MEGA MOOSE MYSTERY

HERO MOOSE! PLUS OWL
WWWWWWWW

WANTED!

WANTED!

BREAKING NEWS! Camo Chameleon at large! (Even though he's very small!) WWWWWWW
WWWWWWW WWWWW
WWWWWWW

"I'm glad the moose solved the crime but overall, I think I still like chocolate mousse better. You don't happen to have any, do you? In the shiny gold wrappers?" Barry the Barracuda.
Chocolate Mousse not available for comment.

MOOSE ON A MISSION

WITH ART BY

Mo O'Hara　**Jess Bradley**

To my brother Matt, who introduced me
to comics and graphic novels and is my hero.
—M. O.

For Emma, without whom my childhood
would have been far duller (but also
with far less NKOTB). Miss you.
—J. B.

Special Agent Anonymoose Personnel File

Size: Extremely large

Distinguishing features: Antlers, dark brown hide, small birthmark that looks a little like North Dakota

Talents: Master of disguise, spying, investigating the strange (and possibly strange) goings-on in Woodland Territories, world-renowned Twister player

Favorite item of clothing: Snazzy investigating suit with lots of important pockets for spy stuff

Clearance for spying: First Class Spy Clearance for secrets

Clearance for height: About seven and a half feet

Not-Quite-So-Special Agent Owlfred Personnel File

Size: Small enough that he can fit in a moose's pocket

Distinguishing features: Gray, feathery, can do that crazy owl thing where they twist their head most of the way around (but it makes him slightly motion sick)

Talents: Very precise analysis of clues and data, calm attitude in a crisis, patience in a crisis (also very good at just avoiding crises)

Favorite item of clothing: Exceedingly tiny bowler hat that he's been told accentuates his fetching feathery ears

Clearance for spying: Third Class Spy Clearance for secrets

Clearance for height: Irrelevant due to flying and all

Chapter 1

Agent Moose, Agent Moose,
A master of disguise.
Agent Moose, Agent Moose,
The best of forest spies.
There's no mystery too tricky,
No clue that can't be found,
No plan that can't be foiled,
With Anonymoose around.

Theme tune ideas

MUSICAL MOOSE

Anonymoose, I know things are a bit slow at the moment, but...why is there a barbershop quartet of magpies singing about you?

Don't you just love the magpies' song, Owlfred? I thought I needed a theme tune, so I hired them. You remember them from the Case of the Missing Shiny Things?

Yes, case 87.

Flip!

:Found!:

Hi there. I thought I would stop by to see what's going on at Woodland HQ. Any stories brewing?

No stories brewing—just hot cocoa.

Yes, please, Owlfred. Seven sugars. I can't stop for stories now, Newt. I have family coming to visit and a theme tune to listen to. I'm a very busy moose, you know.

Oh, and here's your shiny watch back, Anonymoose.

How did you...? Never mind...

Jumping jackrabbits, I'm late! I need to get to the train station.

Jumping jackrabbits sounds like the title of a song.

I think it's just an expression.

No, he means he's going to catch a lift with the jumping jackrabbits. They are surprisingly swift. Even with a moose on their backs. I think I'll fly—I tend to get motion sick with all that jumping.

No time to fly. We need to meet that train!

Oooooohh deeeeeear!!!!!!!

Yank!

What did her message say? Exactly?

Anonymoose
Big Woods

So excited to see my little Moosey Goosey in the Big Woods! Meet me at the station, I'll drop in around noon.

Granny
XXX

The Magnificent Mooseini

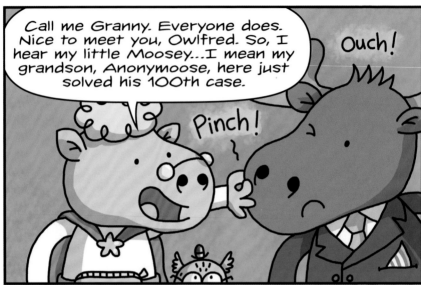

Oh, you'd never get Anonymoose up there. I remember we tried to get you on the trapeze one time when you visited the circus, and you just hung there with your eyes closed saying "Pleeeeeeease get me down. I'm tall enough when I'm on the ground."

Are you scared of heights, Anonymoose?

I just have a healthy respect for anything taller than my antlers.

Granny Moose is a circus stunt moose. She does all kinds of tricks and stunts.

But I'm retiring now. The circus is in town and my last performance is tonight.

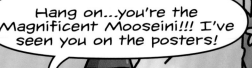

Agent Moose. We're sorry to intrude on family time, but there is an urgent mission that needs your attention. Animals in the forest are terrified. They are being intimidated into giving up their prize possessions by someone, but they are too afraid to say who is scaring them. You need to find out who is putting the squeeze on these forest animals and put a stop to it. This could be a dangerous character, Anonymoose, so use utmost caution.

This message will be sucked up by an anteater in one second.

Slup!

The message pods. They weren't good for her digestion so she transferred departments. She's in Data Analysis now, I think.

Oh, I love Data Analysis! All that data! All that analyzing! ⇒sigh⇐

$x + y = \dfrac{27}{2} + \dfrac{3}{54}$

0.004
6.738
4.956
0.988

467

$\sqrt{0.25}$

And I love investigating. Let's find out who is putting the squeeze on the animals of the Big Woods.

Well, I still want to come along and see my Nony investigate something.

Granny, we can't take you along on official Woodland HQ business. What if you got hurt?

Anony, honey, I've been in more dangerous situations than you've rubbed fuzz off your antlers.

Along for the Ride

So, where are we going to start the investigation, Anonymoose?

We need to question the animals that were intimidated into giving away their things.

I'll make a list of all the animals who have been robbed! I do like making lists.

HELLO! ANY CRIMINALS STILL AROUND?

Wooooooo!

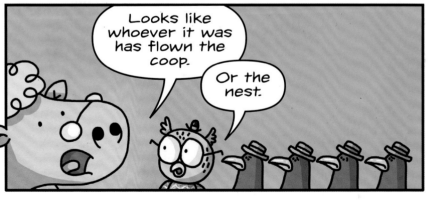

Looks like whoever it was has flown the coop.

Or the nest.

By using a time-honored crime-solving technique that sleuths have used for decades...

And what's that?

We're going to blend in with the witnesses so they'll relax and, hopefully, reveal the robber. Then we'll meet you and Newt at the cocoa shop. And I think I know just where to start!

knows what's coming!

Several Tupperware containers of food.

A crate of coconuts.

A pirate hat.

A feather boa.

Oh, and a deed to a time-share property in the Hamptons.

What can we say? We find a lot of stuff.

This is very nice of you both, but they won't talk. This robber has all the witnesses so scared that they all clam up.

Literally. Clem the Clam had his pearl stolen yesterday and even he's not talking.

And I can go to the Woodland HQ data archive and see what I can find out about a snake who puts the squeeze on people. Maybe they have a record?

So, Anonymoose... you know what would be a fun game?

Filing!! Yaaay! Fun with Filing! Doesn't that sound like a great game, Anonymoose?

It only works when Granny does it, Owlfred.

Oh. Never mind, then.

While you're out doing your research, I can show Granny around the Big Woods and see if we spot anything out of the ordinary or ask if anyone has seen a snake. I'm a moose on a mission.

We're both moose on a mission. Woooo eeey!

But I do like it here in Data. So you see, if you input the parameters of the investigation, we can calibrate it against the known criminal database, and then, if we're lucky, we'll get a match.

Data Analysis suits you.

That's our snake!!! I must tell Anonymoose. They look dangerous to me. Come on!

Point!

It's funny, there's no one around. Everyone in the Big Woods must be scared. We have to find this snake and find it fast!

I feel like I'm taking you away from your investigating, Nony.

Unless we get a lead on the identity of the robber from Owlfred's data analysis, this investigation has hit a brick wall.

AGENT MOOSE

Name:
Anna-CON-da

Description:
Colorful 15-ft snake
with lots of muscle

Whereabouts:
Recently released
from Woodland Prison.
Whereabouts unknown

Hobbies:
Accordion playing. Making fresh-
squeezed orange juice

Criminal Convictions:
Robbery, intimidation of forest animals

MO (Most Obvious way
of doing crimes):
Putting the squeeze on folks and
forcing them to give away their
possessions

The Big Squeeze

The Big Squeeze

The Big Squeeze

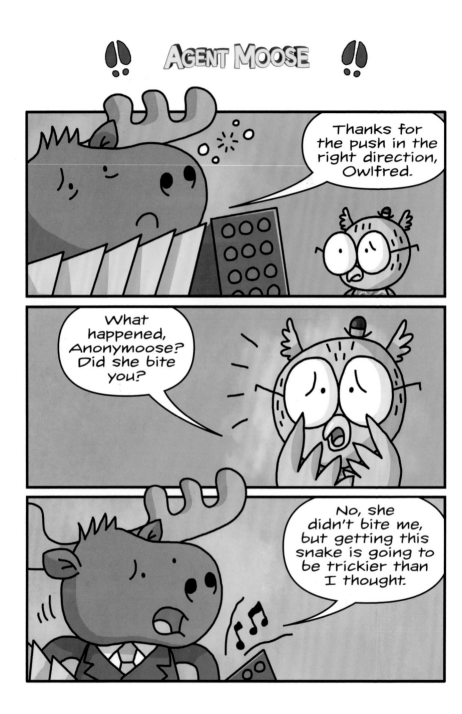

We need to figure out where she'll strike next and be there waiting for her. Lay a different trap.

I think I might have an idea.

Where?

Anna-con-da is definitely going to want more stuff to steal. She's taken almost everything from the animals of the Big Woods. She needs something new.

And what's just arrived at the forest with lots of stuff to steal?

Point!

CIRCUS

The Big Squeeze

Chapter 8

TREASURE HUNT

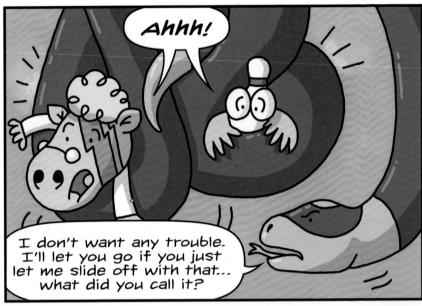

AGENT MOOSE

Snakes and Ladders

Don't worry. Now that Anonymoose is in pursuit, she's as good as caught. Right, Anonymoose? Anonymoose? What happened?

I looked down.

AGENT MOOSE

Anonymoose? Quick. Anna-con-da is getting away. We have to chase her across the rope.

HIGH STAKES HIGH WIRE

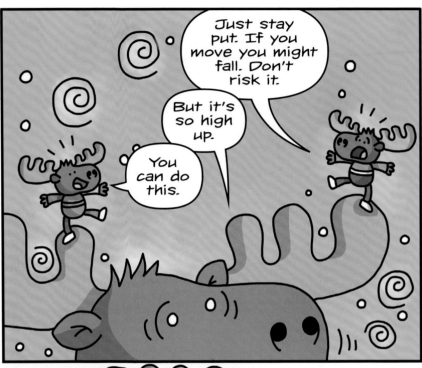

AGENT MOOSE

High Stakes High Wire

AGENT MOOSE

AGENT MOOSE

High Stakes High Wire

LAIRS AND LOOT

You have really nice stuff, but it was wrong of me to take it. And wrong of me to put the squeeze on you to stay quiet about it. If I get anxious, I just can't help squeezing. I was so scared that if anyone knew I was stealing I would have to go back to jail.

Well, at least you recognize that you were wrong.

You scared a lot of animals though, Anna-con-da.

Sometimes I don't know my own strength. I promise I won't put the squeeze on any more animals. I'm sorry I scared everyone. What can I do to make it up to everyone?

Well, you could put your squeezing to good use.

Yes, instead of going back to prison, maybe you could help out here.

☆ Backstage ☆

That was amazing. And we get to do that every day? As a job?

Sure. When you're not helping out the other animals.

You're a natural stunt snake. I spotted your potential the first time you coiled us up to the trapeze platform.

My little Nony! Now I can retire happy—once I've trained Anna-con-da to be the best darn stunt snake in the business, of course. Anytime you want to join me on the tightrope, Nony, just let me know.

Hug!

I think I'm fine on the ground really. In the future I'll try and leave the flying to Owlfred.

That's good. I don't fancy any more jumping jackrabbits for a while.

Or right above me, maybe? The bears said they would give us a lift back on the scenic route along the tracks. Fancy a ride home?

Geronimoooooooooooooooooose!!!

Ahem...
Woooo eeey!

AGENT MOOSE
OPERATION OWL

WITH ART BY

Mo O'Hara   **Jess Bradley**

To my son, Dan, who always inspires me
—M. O.

For Mum, Dad, and Ben x
—J. B.

FOREST BOOK 🌲

☺ ANONYMOOSE ♥ 7

Check out this cool detective selfie!

☺ ANONYMOOSE ♥ 10

My best bud!

Special Agent Anonymoose
Personnel File:

Size: Extremely large

Distinguishing features:
Antlers, dark brown hide,
small birthmark that looks a
little like North Dakota

Talents: Master of
disguise, spying,
investigating the strange
(and possibly strange)
goings on in Woodland
Territories, world-
renowned Twister player

Favorite Movie: The Moose
with the Golden Antlers

Clearance for spying: First
Class Spy Clearance for
secrets

Clearance for height:
About seven and a half feet

FOREST BOOK 🌲

 🙂 OWLFRED ♥ 9

New calculator!!!

🙂 OWLFRED ♥ 12

Nothing like a hot cup of cocoa!

Not-Quite-So-Special Agent Owlfred Personnel File:

Size: Small enough that he can fit in a moose's pocket

Distinguishing features: Gray, feathery, can do that crazy owl thing where they twist their head most of the way around (but it makes him slightly motion sick)

Talents: Very precise analysis of clues and data, calm attitude in a crisis, patience in a crisis (also very good at just avoiding crisis)

Favorite Movie: For Your Owls Only

Clearance for spying: Third Class Spy Clearance for secrets

Clearance for height: Irrelevant due to flying and all

Chapter 1

☆ NEWS OF THE WILD ☆

FLUKE FLASH FLOOD FLUMMOXES FAMOUS ── MOOSE! ──

"I was NOT Flummoxed!!"

〜〜〜〜〜〜〜〜〜〜〜〜〜〜〜〜
〜〜〜〜〜〜〜〜〜〜〜〜〜〜〜〜
〜〜〜〜〜〜〜〜〜〜〜〜〜〜〜〜
〜〜〜〜〜〜〜〜〜〜〜〜〜〜〜〜
〜〜〜〜〜〜〜〜〜〜〜〜〜〜〜〜
〜〜〜〜〜〜〜〜〜〜〜〜〜〜〜〜

Water Wrecks Woods!

〜〜〜〜〜〜〜〜〜〜〜〜〜〜〜
〜〜〜〜〜〜〜〜〜〜〜〜〜〜〜
〜〜〜〜〜〜〜〜〜〜〜〜〜〜〜
〜〜〜〜〜〜〜〜〜〜〜〜〜〜〜
〜〜〜〜〜〜〜〜〜〜〜〜〜〜〜

FLUKE FLOOD

I don't agree with your headline, Newt... Well, I agree I am indeed a famous moose, but not flummoxed!

Do you know what that means, Anonymoose?

Yes...no... mostly. I don't think it sounds good.

It means you are bewildered... stumped by the cause of the flood.

I've never been stumped, just slightly annoyed.

Fluke Flood

Well, erm... I think feisty is overrated. Great if you are a Viking but less so if you are an owl who is a respectable Woodland HQ agent.

Sigh...

Maybe you're right, but an owl can dream!

So, Newt, do you recognize the disguise?

Fluke Flood

I never got to take the longboat disguise out on the water so I thought this would be a good chance to test it out. Feel the lapping of the water... well, lapping against my lap.

Does it keep the water out?

Slightly soggy around the middle but mostly watertight!

Squish!

Fluke Flood

No, we're not stealing... we're just...

Tidying up!

uh-huh!

We better get to the bank and see what happened!

Splish!

Maybe we should ask that anteater with the snorkel?

They are leaving us clues in rhyme?

Watch Out! Watch Out!

Poetic clues?

Poetic clues? Hey, that's big news!

Sorry, I can't resist a good rhyme or alliteration. It's like making headlines... Rhyming Robber Muddles Moose!

I'm not muddled!!

So, we need you to investigate this flood at the bank, Agent Moose. We can't let our guard down if there is indeed a villain about. This message will be sucked up by an anteater in five seconds.

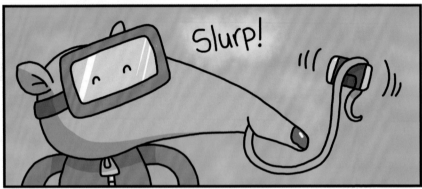

Slurp!

No time to lose! Let's get to the bank!

Moose determination!

Fluke Flood

Can we get back to the hit on the bank?

It was the strangest thing. This wall of water just hit the bank and all the vaults got flooded. While we were in such a panic trying to get stuff up on dry land, we think someone scooped up a lot of the money.

They weren't singing and picking up shiny things, were they?

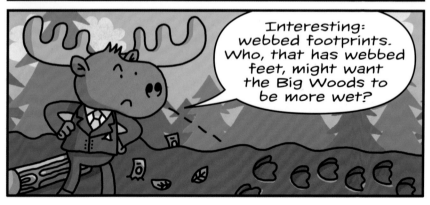

Bank Break-In

Not much, we were... you know... just paddling along and we saw that something happened at the bank. You see anything?

Anything suspicious?

Well, that's a big word for such a cute little duckling!

Pat pat!

Madam, no! —

Oh no, these floods are a right pain in the tail feathers. It's messed up our nesting sites, and look how muddy it all is. I like a nice clean stream.

Yeah, all the ducks were complaining about the floods.

Ah, that's that idea out the window, then.

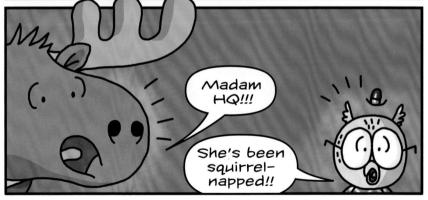

The whole of Woodland HQ was hit with a flash flood!

Cogs Whirring →

There seems to be a lot of that going around.

We have to get our skates on and get to Woodland HQ.

Splish Splish!

You're right! There's no time to lose! Anonymoose, what are you doing?

Data Drama

Data Drama

It looks like you saved a lot of data, Chipmunk. We'll have to wade through it and see what we can find out.

That's funny, Owlfred. Wade through it!

You made a joke, Owlfred?

I guess I did! Not feisty but funny. That's a start!

But maybe some of the data can help us find out what happened to Madam HQ.

Data Drama

Data Drama

Trap Trouble

Trap Trouble

Trap Trouble

And then while he's trying to save Madam HQ he won't suspect what will hit the Big Woods next...

Shhhh!! That part I DON'T want him to know!!

.. - .../.-/-
.-..-.--.*
*It's a trap!

Tap! Tap!

Slam!

☆ 313 ☆

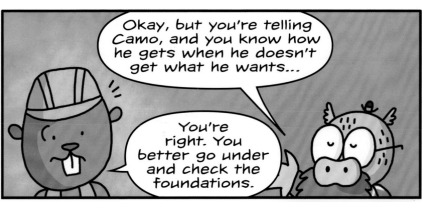

AGENT MOOSE

Secret Schemes

Secret Schemes

Thank you, Paula. That will shut up that little annoying Owlfred while we pay a visit to the REAL Madam HQ. Come on, Paula.

The REAL Madam HQ?

Secret Schemes

Mr. Chameleon, Madam HQ has been expecting you.

Gah!

This way.

Hmpf!

What did I miss?

AGENT MOOSE

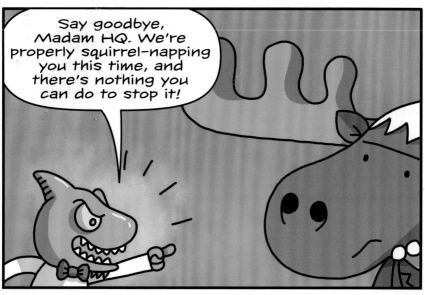

Say goodbye, Madam HQ. We're properly squirrel-napping you this time, and there's nothing you can do to stop it!

Ha ha ha ha ha ha HA HA HA HA!!

AGENT MOOSE

Chapter 8

TELLING TALES

Good work, Paula. We can't have those magpies ruining my plan before Anonymoose finds out.

Yes, about that...

Shhh. It is strange, though, that they said, "Owlfred is going to stop it."

Chapter 9

DAM DISASTER

Dam Disaster

Dam Disaster

Costume Competition

AGENT MOOSE

So, you're tied. One win each. Whoever wins this round of the Disguise-a-rama wins the challenge!

This time, let's make it someone we both know. You choose!

Anyone?

As long as we both know them.

GLARE!

Okay, I think I know this one pretty well...

← Smug!

Costume Competition

We have to go now!! The annoying little owl and the chipmunk have wrecked the dam. It collapsed! No flood!

Hee hee! I mean... grrr!

They foiled my plan?! So what did you do with the owl and the chipmunk then?

Ugh, it's Camo!

Camo, you are under arrest for trying to flood the Big Woods.

Double grrr!

And stealing from the bank to pay the beavers.

And kidnapping the actual real Madam HQ!

Costume Competition

Stop that chameleon!!!

What?!

Camo. You admitted yourself that I was the real Camo so therefore, by the official Disguise-a-rama rules...I win!

NOO!!

I coulda sworn it was you...

You are making it worse!

Costume Competition

He did get your smirk just right...

Argh! You haven't seen the last of me, Anonymoose!

That's so true, because he's right there!

Double argh!!

And thank you, Agent Moose, for saving me. Although I would like to say that you didn't quite capture the full poofiness of my tail in your disguise.

We had a lot of help from the team! Nice touch with the flint fire!

That's straight out of the agents' manual. The chapter "How to Escape."

Do you think I could get a copy of that manual to read in prison? Might come in handy.

NO!

Costume Competition

Owlfred! You led a mission and saved us all! Feisty and clever!

Chipmunk was brilliant, too!

I think you all deserve a medal. Maybe it's time we promoted you, Owlfred, from "Not Quite So Special Agent" to "Quite Special Agent"?

☆GASP!☆

And thank you to all the other Woodland HQ agents and animals...

And me?

Everyone!!

Ahhhhhh!

Snap!

Say cheese! That will be on the front cover tomorrow!

☆ 379 ☆

Now that the Big Woods is safe, why don't we drop Camo and Paula at Woodland Prison, and make sure the beavers give the money back and help repair everything as punishment!

I have some ideas on how to rebuild and upgrade Woodland HQ!

And then we can all go for hot cocoa to celebrate.

With marshmallows?

And extra feisty sprinkles!

That sounds like an excellent plan. And I do like a plan!

★ NEWS of the WILD ★

CAMO CAPTURED!!! PAULA IN PRISON!

Master criminals caught by Agent Moose and other members of Woodland HQ today after a confounding kidnap caper. Agent Moose: "I was not confounded either!"

Feisty fashion fad-little red beards are all the rage!

Beavers beaver away at fixing flood damage

Chipmunk designs new Data Room for rebuilt Woodland HQ!

THANK YOU FOR READING.

The Friends who made

possible are:

Jean Feiwel, Publisher

Liz Szabla, Associate Publisher

Rich Deas, Senior Creative Director

Holly West, Senior Editor

Anna Roberto, Senior Editor

Kat Brzozowski, Senior Editor

Dawn Ryan, Executive Managing Editor

Kim Waymer, Senior Production Manager

Erin Siu, Associate Editor

Emily Settle, Associate Editor

Rachel Diebel, Assistant Editor

Foyinsi Adegbonmire, Associate Editor

Liz Dresner, Associate Art Director

Mandy Veloso, Senior Production Editor